Learn about

COLORS

World Book, Inc.
525 W. Monroe
Chicago, IL 60661

For information on other
World Book products,
call 1-800-255-1750.

ISBN: 0-7166-6103-9
LC: 95-61313

Printed in Mexico

1 2 3 4 5 6 7 8 9 10 99 98 97 96 95

Learn about
COLORS

World Book, Inc.
a Scott Fetzer company
Chicago London Sydney Toronto

Meet Poldy
and his friends

Poldy the scarecrow was made to scare birds away from a farmer's field. But the birds were not frightened by Poldy. In fact, three birds named Wagtail, Crow, and Seagull became his friends.

When the weather grew cold, Poldy's friends prepared to fly away to wonderful, warm places all over the world. The three birds wanted Poldy to go with them, so they worked together to teach him how to fly. Then Poldy and his friends flew away to see and learn about the world.

In **Learn about Colors**, Poldy and his friends visit a South American rain forest.

Poldy and the birds flew
a long, long way. They flew
over mountains and seas.
The wind tugged at Poldy's
hat and pulled at his straw
hair. Worst of all, it made his
eyes water.

"Do you think we could land?" he asked at last. "I'd like to rest."

"We'll be landing soon," announced Crow. Far below them, thick forests stretched as far as the eye could see.

"But where shall we land?" asked Poldy, as he searched the ground for a small, clear space.

"On a tree, of course," snapped Seagull.

"Oh, dear!" said Poldy, who had never landed on a tree in his life.

The birds dived down and landed on the cushion of leaves. One, two, three.

But Poldy tumbled right through the cushion of leaves and landed, *bump*, on the forest floor.

It was very dark in the forest. It was very dark indeed!

Poldy rubbed his eyes.
He couldn't see a thing.

"Peekaboo!" said a voice.
Poldy saw a flash of yellow.

Poldy saw a flash of red.

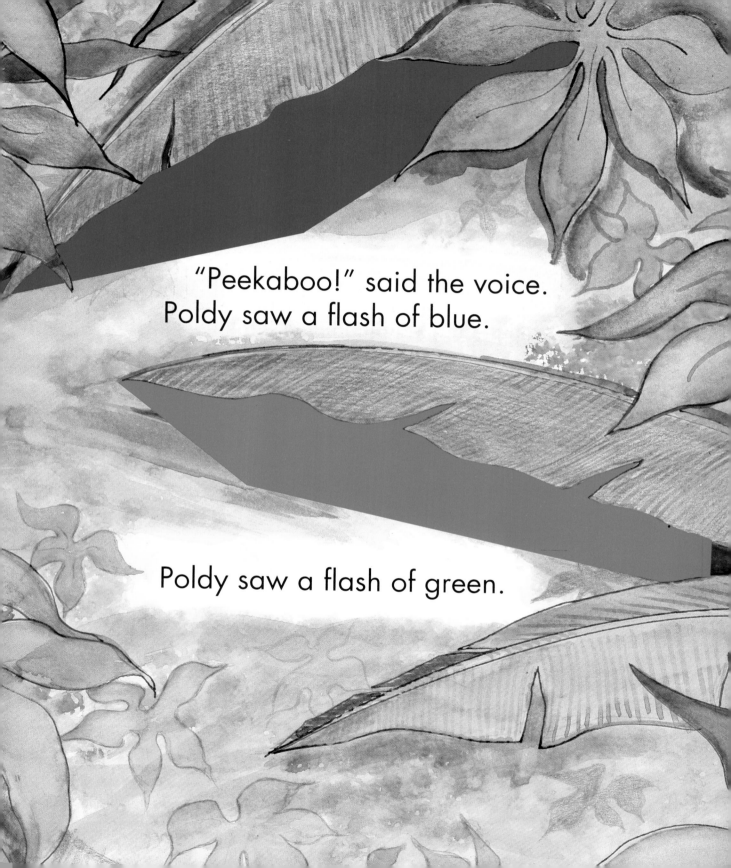

"Peekaboo!" said the voice.
Poldy saw a flash of blue.

Poldy saw a flash of green.

"Who's there?" asked
Seagull, pecking angrily
at Poldy's hat.

"Who's there?" asked Crow, peering into the darkness.

"Who's there?" asked Wagtail, fluttering down to hide in Poldy's sleeve.

"It's me!" said a parrot.
"Didn't you guess?"

"You're so beautiful!" said Wagtail. "Your colors are so bright."

"I need my bright colors in the dark forest," said the parrot, "so that my friends can find me."

"Peekaboo!" said all
the parrots.

"Peekaboo!" said two children. "We live in the forest, too. We were hiding in the trees. We don't wear lots of clothes like you do, Poldy. We paint our bodies with colors."

Poldy thought this sounded like fun. "Will you paint me, too?" he asked.

"This is blue," said the children. "We will paint the blue of the sky and the blue of the river."

"This is yellow," said the children. "We will paint the yellow of the butterflies and the yellow of the sun."

"This is black, made from the ashes of the fire. We will paint the shadows of the trees and the dark stripes of the bees."

"This is red. We will
paint the red of the beads."

"We can mix blue and yellow together to make green. We will paint the green of the leaves."

"We can mix red and yellow together to make orange. We will paint the orange of the birds."

"We can mix red and blue together to make purple. We will paint the purple of the flowers."

Poldy looked at his reflection in the river. He looked like the sky, the trees, the leaves, and the flowers.

"Where are you?" called the birds. "Where are you, Poldy?"

Splash! Poldy fell into the river, and all his colors washed away.

"So there you are," snapped Seagull, "playing around in the water."

"No, he's taking a bath," said Crow. "Why don't we join him?"

Parent notes

Learn about Colors tells of Poldy's adventures in a rain forest. As the title suggests, the story will teach your child about colors. There are two parts to the story. The first part introduces each of the primary colors and the color black. In the second part, primary colors are mixed together to make secondary colors.

As you read through the story, you will find many opportunities for discussion with your child. Ask your child to follow the pictures and find the colors in the story. As children become familiar with the story, they will begin to ask questions of their own. Here are some other starting points for discussion:

All about the forest

Do you know what a forest is?

Have you ever been in a forest?

Is it dark there?

Why do you think it is dark?

Can you think of any other dark places?

What can we do to make a dark place lighter?

What colorful things live in a forest?

All about the parrots

Did you like the parrots?

Why did you like them?

What colors are the parrots' feathers?

Can you think of any other colorful animals?

Learning together

Colored paints or crayons will give your child the opportunity to mix and experiment with colors and shades. You can use powder paints, block paints, watercolors, oil-based and wax crayons, soft pencils, and chalk. Make sure that tables and clothes are well covered so that your child need not worry about making a mess. Here are some other activities using colors:

Use food dyes in water. A couple of drops of different colors will swirl and float together in an exciting and intriguing way. Ask your child to describe what is happening to the colors.

Make a color scrapbook together by cutting out and collecting a set of pictures about each color. This will help your child to develop skills in sorting and cutting, too.

When you are out walking together, look for different colors. See how many you can remember when you get home.

Try using colored plastic wrap to make a pair of color glasses. Let your child see how the color glasses change the way things look. Ask your child to describe what he or she can see.

Play *Color I Spy*. Begin by choosing an object you can see, then say, "I spy, with my little eye, something that is the color . . ." and tell your child the color. The idea of the game is for children to take turns guessing the object from the color clue.